# Animal Teachers

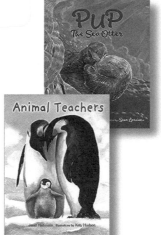

## Description

Students begin by exploring the phenomenon of a mother sea otter interacting with her pup. Through texts, videos, and discussion of sea otters as well as emperor penguins, sea turtles, and a variety of other animals, students identify patterns in the behaviors of both parents and offspring that help offspring survive. They elaborate on this idea by playing a game to model how penguin chicks and their parents use vocalizations to find each other within large groups.

## Alignment With the *Next Generation Science Standards*

| Performance Expectation | | |
| --- | --- | --- |
| 1-LS1-2: Read texts and use media to determine patterns in behavior of parents and offspring that help offspring survive. | | |

| Science and Engineering Practice | Disciplinary Core Idea | Crosscutting Concept |
| --- | --- | --- |
| Obtaining, Evaluating, and Communicating Information Read grade-appropriate texts and/or use media to obtain scientific and/or technical information to determine patterns in and/or evidence about the natural and designed world(s). | LS1.B: Growth and Development of Organisms Adult plants and animals can have young. In many kinds of animals, parents and the offspring themselves engage in behaviors that help the offspring to survive. | Patterns Patterns in the natural world can be observed, used to describe phenomena, and used as evidence. |

Note: The activities in this lesson will help students move toward the performance expectations listed, which is the goal after multiple activities. However, the activities will not by themselves be sufficient to reach the performance expectations.

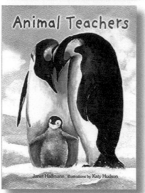

# Featured Picture Books

TITLE: **Pup the Sea Otter**
AUTHOR: **Jonathan London**
ILLUSTRATOR: **Sean London**
PUBLISHER: **WestWinds Press**
YEAR: **2017**
GENRE: **Narrative Information**
SUMMARY: *Spare, poetic text and vibrant illustrations tell the story of a sea otter's first year, from birth to first dive to young adulthood.*

TITLE: **Animal Teachers**
AUTHOR: **Janet Halfmann**
ILLUSTRATOR: **Katy Hudson**
PUBLISHER: **Blue Apple**
YEAR: **2014**
GENRE: **Non-Narrative Information**
SUMMARY: *This book reveals the many ways animal parents teach their babies the behaviors they need to survive.*

## Time Needed

This lesson will take several class periods. Suggested scheduling is as follows:

Session 1: Engage with Pup the Sea Otter Read-Aloud and Explore with Sea Otter Video and Sea Turtle Video

Session 2: Explain with Finding Patterns and Animal Teachers Read-Aloud

Session 3: Elaborate with Penguin Songs

Session 4: Evaluate with Animal Teacher Posters

## Materials

Per student

- Elastic "ouchless" headband or black construction paper strip (approx. 2" × 11") to make a headband
- Crayons or markers (you will need extra gray and black)
- Scissors
- Tape

**SAFETY**
- Use caution when working with scissors (a potential sharp hazard) to avoid cutting or puncturing skin.
- Have students wash hands with soap and water after completing activities.

National Science Teaching Association

## Student Pages

- Penguin Adult Headband or Penguin Chick Headband (Half the class will be "parents," and the other half will be "chicks.")
- Penguin Songs (Pre-cut the cards. If you have more than 24 students or if you have an odd number of students, cut out additional "adult" cards.)
- Animal Teacher
- STEM Everywhere

## Background for Teachers

How do baby animals survive? In many kinds of animals, parents do not care for their young once they are born, so babies must be born in an advanced physical state and possess strong survival instincts. Instinct is the ability to perform a behavior the first time an animal is exposed to the proper stimulus—in other words, in the absence of learning. For example, newly hatched sea turtles will instinctively move toward the ocean. Baby spiders instinctively know how to spin webs. Snakelets instinctively know how to find food. And although some of these animals receive a degree of parental care before they are born (via nesting or guarding behaviors), none of these animals needs to be taught to survive by a parent.

In other kinds of animals, parental care is critical to the survival of offspring. The advantage of a species engaging in parental care is that it can increase the chances that offspring will survive to reproduce and pass on the parents' genes. Parental care is rare in fish and amphibians but occurs in some reptiles such as crocodilians. It is most evident in birds and mammals. Parental care may include teaching offspring to walk, swim, fly, forage, hunt, fight, evade predators, use tools, build nests, socialize, and communicate.

The degree of parental care varies greatly from one species of animal to another. Some animal babies (including humans!) are born helpless and completely reliant on their parent(s). A baby kangaroo, called a joey, is blind, hairless, and only a few centimeters long at birth. Guided by instinct, it must crawl to the mother's pouch and attach to a teat, where it remains for several months. A newborn orangutan cannot even raise its head and is completely dependent on its mother for care and feeding. Baby orangutans nurse for four to five years (the longest of any primate) and rely on their mothers for transport, comfort, and safety for six to eight years. Orangutan mothers are excellent teachers, modeling what and how to eat (including the use of tools to get food), how to build elaborate sleeping nests, and how to avoid predators. Other animal babies require parental care but are born able to walk or feed themselves. A chick can walk and peck for food soon after hatching but must stay with its mother for protection for about two months. An elephant calf, the largest baby born on land, can walk nearly a mile at only a day old but is dependent on its mother's milk for the first year of life.

All marine mammal species give some degree of parental care. A mother dolphin helps nudge a newborn calf to the surface to breathe and quickly teaches it to find her by whistling. She nurses her calf for two to three years. During this time, she teaches it how to interact with other dolphins, how to find and catch prey, how to avoid dangers, and how to navigate. A sea otter pup is born with eyes open, first teeth already emerging, and a full coat of dense fur that enables it to float, but the pup is otherwise completely dependent on its mother, who nurses the pup while floating on her back. The mother otter often wraps her pup in strands of kelp (seaweed) to keep it from drifting. If she senses danger, she will grab the pup by its neck and dive underwater until the danger has passed. She teaches her pup to swim, dive, find food, and even use rocks to break shells. The pup is ready to live independently when it reaches six to eight months of age.

Biparental care, in which both the male and female contribute to feeding and guarding the offspring, is the most common form of parental care in birds. Penguin mating pairs exhibit a very high degree of biparental care. The male emperor penguin keeps a newly laid egg warm by balancing it on his feet and covering it with a very warm layer of feathered skin known as a brood pouch. He eats nothing for two months while he is caring for the egg. Meanwhile, the female devotes this time to replenishing her food reserves in the open sea. If the chick hatches before the female returns, the male, despite his fasting, is able to secrete a substance from his esophagus to feed the chick, keeping it alive for up to two weeks. When the female returns, she brings a belly full of food which she regurgitates for the newly hatched chick. The mother then feeds and cares for the chick while the male takes his turn at sea. As the chicks grow larger, adult emperors leave them in groups called crèches when they leave to fish. The chicks huddle together for warmth and often wander around waiting to hear the call of a returning parent. Penguin families can recognize members by their distinctive calls. By the time the chicks are five months old, they are completely independent from their parents.

In this lesson, students explore the ways in which sea otters, emperor penguins, and many other animals care for their offspring. Students use the science and engineering practice (SEP) of obtaining, evaluating, and communicating information as they listen to texts and watch video clips of animals and their young. They also apply the crosscutting concept (CCC) of patterns as they determine patterns of behavior in both parents and offspring that help the offspring survive, for example, instinctive behaviors (nest building in mother sea turtles, climbing out of the nest and crawling to the ocean in baby sea turtles); vocalizations that offspring make (sea otter pups crying, penguin chicks chirping); and the responses of the parents (feeding, comforting, and protecting the offspring).

## Learning Progressions

Below are the disciplinary core idea (DCI) grade band endpoints for grades K–2 and 3–5. These are provided to show how student understanding of the DCIs in this lesson will progress in future grade levels.

| DCI | Grades K–2 | Grades 3–5 |
| --- | --- | --- |
| LS1.B: Growth and Development of Organisms | • Adult plants and animals can have young. In many kinds of animals, parents and the offspring themselves engage in behaviors that help the offspring to survive. | • Reproduction is essential to the continued existence of every kind of organism. Plants and animals have unique and diverse life cycles. |

Source: Willard, T., ed. 2015. The NSTA quick-reference guide to the NGSS: Elementary school. Arlington, VA: NSTA Press.

# engage

*Pup the Sea Otter* **Read-Aloud**

### Making Connections: Text to Self

Before reading, ask

? Have you ever helped take care of a baby animal? What kind? (Answers will vary.)

? How did you take care of it? (gave it food, water, protection, shelter, etc.)

? In what ways do animal parents care for their young (which is another word for babies)? (they feed them, protect them, keep them warm, teach them, etc.)

? Have you ever seen a sea otter? (Answers will vary.)

? How do sea otters take care of their babies? (Answers will vary.)

---

**SEP: Obtaining, Evaluating, and Communicating Information**
Read grade-appropriate texts to obtain scientific information to determine patterns in and/or evidence about the natural world.

---

Then tell students you have a book to share that describes how a mother sea otter takes care of her baby, which is called a pup. Introduce the author and illustrator of Pup the Sea Otter. Students might be interested to know that the author and illustrator are a father-son team!

---

Connecting to the Common Core
**Reading: Informational Text**
KEY IDEAS AND DETAILS: 1.2

---

### Determining Importance

Ask students to listen for how the mother teaches and takes care of her baby as you read the book aloud. Then ask

? What was the main idea of the book? (how sea otters take care of their pups, sea otters are good mothers, etc.)

? What did you notice about how the mother sea otter took care of her pup? (Possible responses could include that the mother nursed pup on her belly, groomed pup, hugged pup, wrapped pup in kelp, protected pup from sharks, etc.)

? What did she teach her pup to do? (swim and find food, use tools to open shells)

? What did you notice about what the baby sea otter did to survive? (Possible responses could include that the baby nuzzled mama's belly (to drink milk), slept on mama's chest, squealed and cried for mama, learned to swim, learned to dive, etc.)

# explore

## Sea Otter Video

*MOTHER SEA OTTER GROOMING HER PUP*

After the read-aloud, tell students they are going to observe a real sea otter and her newborn pup in the wild (on video)! Ask students to look for ways this mother sea otter is taking care of her

baby. Then show the video "Mom and Newborn Sea Otter Pup Getting to Know Each Other" (see the "Websites" section for the video link).

 Questioning

After watching, ask

? How does the mother sea otter in the video take care of her pup? (she holds it on her belly/keeps it out of the water, licks/grooms it)

? Why does she need to take care of the pup? (it is helpless, it needs help, to help it survive, etc.)

? How does a baby sea otter look like its mother? How does it look different? (Same: it is brown, furry, has four legs and a long tail, etc. Different: it is smaller)

? What are you wondering about sea otters? (Answers will vary.)

## Sea Turtle Video

Tell students you have a video about sea turtles. As they watch, have them think about how the mother sea turtle's care for her young is different than the mother sea otter's. Show the "Sea Turtle Nesting" video (see the "Websites" section for the video link).

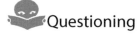 Questioning

After watching, ask

? How does the mother sea turtle in the video protect her eggs? (she digs a nest in the sand, she covers up the nest, she camouflages the nest)

? How does she take care of her young after they hatch? (she doesn't—she leaves after laying the eggs)

? How do the baby sea turtles take care of themselves after they hatch? (they dig out of the nest, they race to the water)

? How does a baby sea turtle look like its mother? How does it look different? (Same: it has a shell, it has four legs and a tail, etc. Different: it is smaller)

? What are you wondering about sea turtles? (Answers will vary.)

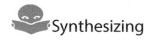 # explain

## Finding Patterns

Explain that sea turtle babies, and many other animal babies, do not receive any care from their parents after they are born. In fact, a mother sea turtle leaves immediately after laying her eggs in the sand, never to see them again. But the babies know how to hatch, dig their way up out of the nest, crawl across the sand, and find the ocean by instinct. They even know how to swim and find food on their own. They do not need a teacher.

Synthesizing

Tell students that now that they have seen videos of two different kinds of animal parents, they can start to look for patterns in how those animals care for their young. Ask

? What do sea turtles and sea otters have in common? (they are both animals, they both live in the ocean or sea, they both eat fish and other sea creatures, they both have young, etc.)

? How is a sea turtle mother different than a sea otter mother? (sea turtles do not take care of their young after they hatch; sea otter mothers spend a long time taking care of and teaching their young)

? How is a sea turtle baby different than a sea otter pup? (a baby sea turtle doesn't need its parents; it can hatch on its own and survive on its own; it doesn't need to be taught how to swim or get food; it can survive by instinct; a sea otter pup needs its mother to survive; and so on)

### *Animal Teachers* Read-Aloud

Making Connections: Text to Self

> **SEP: Obtaining, Evaluating, and Communicating Information**
> Read grade-appropriate texts to obtain scientific information to determine patterns in and/or evidence about the natural world.

Introduce the author and illustrator of Animal Teachers. Tell students that in this book, they will learn about the ways many other animals take care of their young and teach them to survive. Read the first page, and ask

? Who taught you how to do things?

? What things did they teach you?

? Who teaches animals?

> Connecting to the Common Core
> **Reading: Informational Text**
> KEY IDEAS AND DETAILS: 1.1

Explain that in many kinds of animals, such as otters, parents and their young do things that help the young animal survive. Ask students to listen for some ways that these animals help their young survive as you read. Read the book aloud. Be sure to discuss the questions at the end of each section (e.g., Who gave you your first swimming lessons? Can you swim now?).

Questioning

> **CCC: Patterns**
> Patterns in the natural world can be observed, used to describe phenomena, and used as evidence.

After reading, discuss any patterns in parental care the students can identify. Ask

? What do some of the parent animals do that is the same? (e.g., all of the animal parents in the book teach and take care of their young; the prairie dog, penguin, and dolphin parent(s) teach their young to communicate with sounds; the chicken, chimp, and brown bear mothers teach their young to find food, and so on)

*LOOKING FOR PATTERNS*

Revisit the illustrations on each two-page spread, and for each one, ask

? How does the baby animal look like its parent?

? How is it different from its parent?

Examples include the following:

| Animal | Similar to Parent | Different from Parent |
|---|---|---|
| Chick | • Two legs<br>• Feathers | • Smaller body<br>• Shorter beak<br>• Fluffier feathers |
| Bottlenose dolphin calf | • Color<br>• Body shape<br>• Fins | • Smaller body<br>• Shorter beak |
| Cheetah cub | • Spots<br>• Stripes under eyes<br>• Four legs | • Smaller body<br>• Fluffier fur<br>• Shorter tail<br>• Lighter color |

Ask

? Are baby animals exactly like their parents? (No, they are very much, but not exactly, like their parents.)

# elaborate

## Penguin Songs

Reread the two-page spread in Animal Teachers that describes the emperor penguins teaching their chicks to sing. Then explain that after a mother emperor penguin lays an egg, she leaves to hunt for food in the ocean. Meanwhile, the egg is kept warm by the father. He has a feather-lined pouch below his belly that keeps the egg warm. He holds the egg on top of his feet for over two months and doesn't eat anything the whole time! After the chick hatches, the father carries the chick on his feet until the mother penguin returns from the ocean. Penguins live together in very large groups called colonies. So, when the mother returns to feed her chick, she needs to find her mate and her chick among all of the other penguins in the colony. But penguins of the same kind look very much alike.

Then ask

? According to the book, how do penguin families find each other? (with their songs)

Tell students to observe how this looks in the wild as they watch the video "How Penguin Moms Find Their Chicks" (see the "Websites" section for the video link).

 Questioning

Then ask

? What things do emperor penguins do to help the penguin chicks survive? (the fathers carry the chicks on their feet to keep them warm, the fathers line up so the mothers can find them by their distinctive songs/calls, the mothers feed the chicks)

? What do the emperor penguin chicks do to find their parents? (sing/call)

? How is an emperor penguin chick like a sea otter pup? (they are both helpless when they are born or hatched, they both call to their parents, they are both taught by their parents)

> **CCC: Patterns**
> Patterns in the natural world can be observed, used to describe phenomena, and used as evidence.

Then tell students that you are going to play a game to model how penguin families locate each other within a colony of penguins that all look similar. First, divide the class into two groups. In this model, half of the class will portray adult penguins, and the other half will be chicks. Pass out a Penguin Adult Headband student page to each student who will be an adult penguin, and a Penguin Chick Headband student page to each student who will be a penguin chick. Give them time to cut out and color their penguin pictures. Then they can make it a headband either by tucking the picture into an elastic "ouchless" headband or by attaching it to a 2" × 11" strip of a construction paper.

National Science Teaching Association

Next, have students put on their headbands and form two lines—one line of "adults," one line of "chicks"—facing each other from opposite sides of the classroom. Mix up the Penguin Songs cards, then give each "adult" a card with an adult penguin and song on it, and each "chick" a card with a baby penguin and song on it. If you have more than 24 students, or if you have an odd number of students, hand out additional adult penguin cards. Some students will then end up in a group of three: two parents and one chick.

Explain that the goal of the game is to locate the penguin(s) singing the same "song" (e.g., "Chicka-chick-chick?") without talking or looking at each other's cards. This is similar to how real penguins find each other in a crowd. When you say START, students should read the "song" on their card and then walk around the room quietly "singing" until they find the student with the same song. When they do, they should sit down together but keep "singing" quietly in case there is another member of their family to be found. Students will end up in a family of two or three "penguins."

For fun, encourage students to walk like a penguin as they play the game! (They will hold their feet close together and walk by shuffling their feet forward a little at a time.)

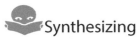 Synthesizing

After all students have found their penguin "family," ask

? How is the game similar to how real penguins find each other in a crowd? (penguins sing or call to each other, penguins "waddle" when they walk, etc.)

? How is it different? (when the chicks are young, they are carried on top of their fathers' feet, and the fathers line up while the mothers walk down the line calling, etc.)

? What other animals find each other by singing or calling? (Answers will vary, but from the book Animal Teachers, they should know that the prairie dog, penguin, and

*Penguin headbands*

dolphin parent(s) communicate with their offspring using sounds.)

? Some animal families locate each other by smell or sight. How do you locate family members when you're in a crowd? (Answers will vary.)

# evaluate

## Animal Teacher Poster

Connecting to the Common Core
**Writing**
Research to Build Knowledge: 1.8

## Writing

Pass out the Animal Teacher student page. Explain that students may choose any animal that teaches its young, whether or not the animal was in the books and videos they saw. Students should draw and label a picture of an animal parent teaching a survival behavior to its young and fill in the sentences "A _____ teaches its young to _____. This helps the baby

*ANIMAL TEACHER POSTER*

_____." Some examples from the reading and/or videos include the following:

- "A penguin father teaches its young to sing. This helps the baby find its parents."

- "An orangutan teaches its young to build a nest. This helps the baby stay dry."

- "A sea otter mother teaches its young to break open shells with a rock. This helps the baby get food."

## STEM Everywhere

Give students the STEM Everywhere student page as a way to involve their families and extend their learning. They can do the activity with an adult helper and share their results with the class. If students do not have access to the internet at home, you may choose to have them complete this activity at school.

## Opportunities for Differentiated Instruction

This box lists questions and challenges related to the lesson that students may select to research, investigate, or innovate. Students may also use the questions as examples to help them generate their own questions. These questions can help you move your students from the teacher-directed investigation to engaging in the science and engineering practices in a more student-directed format.

### Extra Support

For students who are struggling to meet the lesson objectives, provide a question and guide them in the process of collecting research or helping them design procedures or solutions.

### Extensions

For students with high interest or who have already met the lesson objectives, have them choose a question (or pose their own question), conduct their own research, and design their own procedures or solutions.

After selecting one of the questions in this box or formulating their own questions, students can individually or collaboratively make predictions, design investigations or surveys to test their predictions, collect evidence, devise explanations, design solutions, or examine related resources. They can communicate their findings through a science notebook, at a poster session or gallery walk, or by producing a media project.

#### Research

Have students brainstorm researchable questions:

? Emperor penguin fathers help care for their young. What other animal fathers help care for their young?

? Sea turtles do not take care of their young. What other animals do not take care of their young?

? How many different kinds of otters or penguins are there?

#### Investigate

Have students brainstorm testable questions to be solved through science or math:

? Can you make a graph showing the relative sizes of the world's penguins (e.g., from shortest to tallest)?

? Collect photographs of your favorite animal babies. Survey your friends: Which animal baby is the cutest? Graph the results, then analyze your graph. What can you conclude?

? Observe a bird's nest on a webcam. Keep a tally of parenting behaviors you observe. Which behaviors do you observe most often?

#### Innovate

Have students brainstorm problems to be solved through engineering:

? Can you design something to help feed an orphaned baby animal?

? Can you design something to protect an egg from a fall?

? How are sea otters, sea turtles, or penguins tracked in the wild?

## Websites

**How Penguin Moms Find Their Chicks**
*www.youtube.com/watch?v=ECxwzOmIDAU*

**Mom and Newborn Sea Otter Pup Getting to Know Each Other**
*www.youtube.com/watch?v=gS3vDjj6LVI*

**Sea Turtle Nesting Video**
*www.seeturtles.org/sea-turtle-life-cycle*

## More Books to Read

Delano, M. F. 2015. *Baby animals.* Washington, DC: National Geographic Kids.
Summary: Colorful photographs, simple text, and engaging captions describe what a variety of baby animals do, from cuddling in warm dens to swinging in trees. Includes the collective nouns for baby animals, such as foals, fawns, and cubs.

Evans, S. 2016. *Follow me: Animal parents and babies.* Washington, DC: National Geographic Kids.
Summary: An "you read, I read" co-reader format guides children through the book as they learn about animal parents teaching their offspring about the world. Includes color photographs, bold print words, and a short activity at the end of each section.

Jenkins, M. 2002. *The emperor's egg.* Somerville, MA: Candlewick Press.
Summary: This beautifully illustrated picture book describes the unusual parental behavior of emperor penguins, focusing on the male penguins who incubate the eggs on their feet for two months while the females are fishing.

Jenkins, S., and R. Page. 2013. *My first day.* Boston, MA: Houghton Mifflin Harcourt.
Summary: Simple text and Jenkins's signature paper collages reveal the first day of life for a variety of animals, with and without parental care. Each animal narrates its own story of what it could or could not do on day one.

Reidy, J. 2019. *Pup 681: A sea otter rescue story.* New York: Henry Holt and Company.
Summary: Inspired by true events, this heartwarming picture book tells the story of an orphaned sea otter who was rescued on the California coast and taken to the Monterey Bay Aquarium, where she received round-the-clock care.

Tatham, B. 2001. *Penguin chick.* New York: Harper Collins.
Summary: This Let's-Read-and-Find-Out-Science book describes how emperor penguins keep their chicks alive in one of Earth's harshest environments.

*Note:* National Geographic Kids publishes a wide variety of books on sea otters, penguins, sea turtles, dolphins, and many other animals featured in this lesson.

Name: _____

# Penguin Adult Headband

Black

Gray

Yellow

Orange

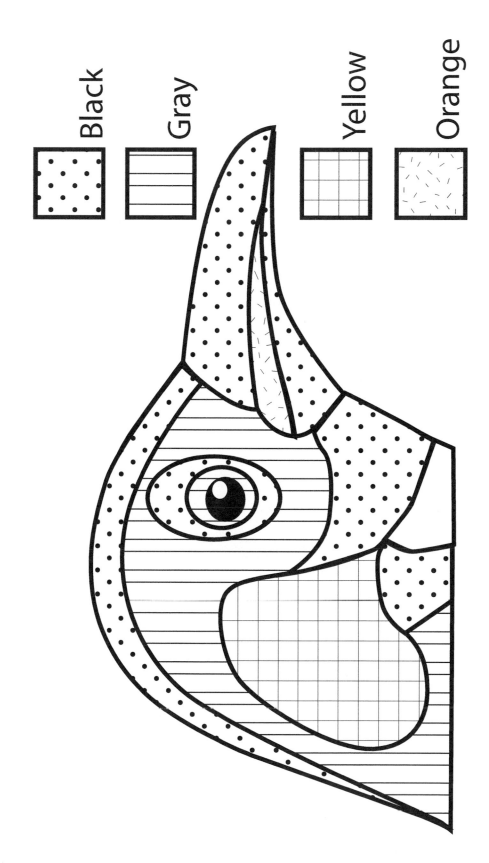

Name: _____

# Penguin Chick Headband

☐ Black

☐ Gray

National Science Teaching Association

# Penguin Songs Set 1

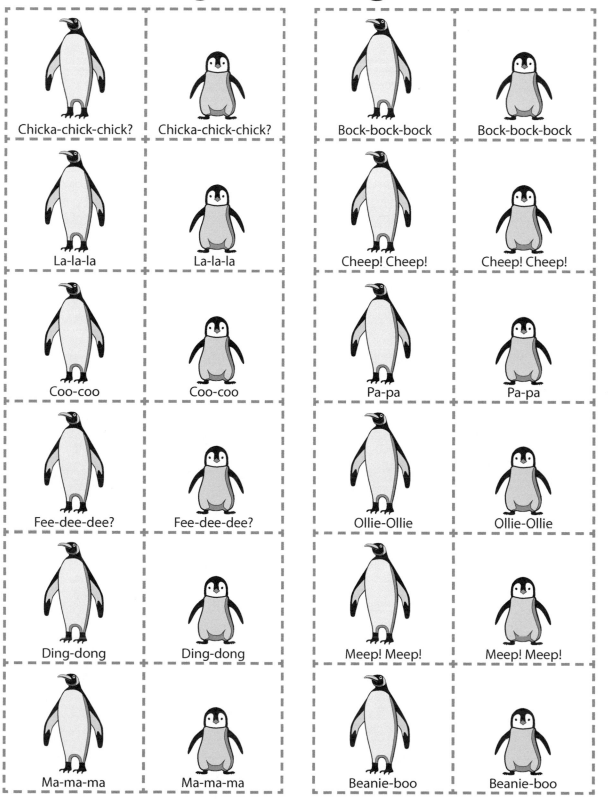

| | | | |
|---|---|---|---|
| Chicka-chick-chick? | Chicka-chick-chick? | Bock-bock-bock | Bock-bock-bock |
| La-la-la | La-la-la | Cheep! Cheep! | Cheep! Cheep! |
| Coo-coo | Coo-coo | Pa-pa | Pa-pa |
| Fee-dee-dee? | Fee-dee-dee? | Ollie-Ollie | Ollie-Ollie |
| Ding-dong | Ding-dong | Meep! Meep! | Meep! Meep! |
| Ma-ma-ma | Ma-ma-ma | Beanie-boo | Beanie-boo |

# Penguin Songs Set 2

| | | | |
|---|---|---|---|
| Peek-a-boo! | Peek-a-boo! | Caw! Caw! | Caw! Caw! |
| Mee-mee-mee | Mee-mee-mee | Zippedy-doo | Zippedy-doo |
| Looky-loo? | Looky-loo? | Ping-goo | Ping-goo |
| Tooty-ta-ta | Tooty-ta-ta | Oopsie | Oopsie |
| Ooo! Ooo! | Ooo! Ooo! | Hee-haw | Hee-haw |
| Bippity-bop | Bippity-bop | Teeny-tiny | Teeny-tiny |

Name: _____

# Animal Teacher

A _____ teaches its young

to _____.

This helps the baby _____.

Name: _____

# STEM Everywhere

Dear Families,

At school, we have been learning how **some animals care for their offspring.** To find out more, ask your learner the following questions and discuss their answers:

- What did you learn?

- What was your favorite part of the lesson?

- What are you still wondering?

 At home, you can watch a marine biologist who takes care of sea otters, then talk about which animals you and your learner would want to take care of at an aquarium or a zoo. What would be fun about the job? What would be hard? To watch the video (available in English and Spanish), scan the QR code or go to *https://cet.pbslearningmedia.org/resource/9457fa09-b5af-46d3-b7fb-d241670ef463/9457fa09-b5af-46d3-b7fb-d241670ef463.*

Brainstorm ideas, then draw and label a picture of you and your learner taking care of a baby animal at a zoo.

National Science Teaching Association